WELCOME TO THE MARVEL™ HEROES

IN THIS ANNUAL YOU WILL FIND...

Throughout the sensational
strip story adventure,
we've hidden this
Fantastic Four logo!
How many can
you find?

£6.99

C000112571

When a threat is too great for one costumed hero, the world turns to earth's mightiest team of superheroes! Introducing the...

AVENGERS

THOR

Norse God of Thunder, Thor is the ruler of the legendary Asgard and one of the greatest superheroes in the universe! Armed with his enchanted Uru hammer Mjolnir, Thor is able to fly, project mystical energy, control storms and even open trans-dimensional portals!

IRON MAN

Tony Stark is a successful inventor and businessman who invented a battle suit that transformed him into the invincible Iron Man! The suit increases Tony's strength to superhuman levels, plus it has various inbuilt weapons and even allows him to fly over 700-mph!

HAWKEYE

Hawkeye is an expert archer with amazing accuracy and reflexes! The modern day Robin Hood also has an array of specialised arrows to defeat his opponents and has also been trained by Captain America in the art of hand-to-hand combat!

CAPTAIN AMERICA

During World War 2, Steve Rogers volunteered to test a new super solider serum, which turned him into the ultimate fighting machine! Equipped with his indestructible shield, Cap leads the Avengers from the front and never backs down from a challenge! He is a true symbol of freedom and liberty!

SCARLET WITCH & QUICKSILVER

It could have been so different for Wanda and Pietro Maximoff. They are the offspring of Magneto, one of the world's most deadly mutants! However, both left their father's Brotherhood of Evil Mutants to join the world's mightiest heroes instead! Wanda can control magic and probability fields, while her brother Pietro possesses superhuman speed!

THE FABULOUS F.F. HOLD A LONG-AWAITED WEDDING!

"FOR BETTER AND FOR WORSE!"

THE MOST SENSATIONAL SUPER-SPECTACULAR EVER WITNESSED BY HUMAN EYES!

DAILY BUGLE EXTRA!

5 CENTS FINAL EDITION

THE PICTURE NEWSPAPER

WEDDING BELL FOR REED & SUE!

SCINTILLATING SCRIPT by **STAN LEE**, PRURIENT PLOT by **FABIAN NICIEZA** PULSE-POUNDING PENCILS (in order of appearance) by **SAL BUSCEMA, JOHN BUSCEMA, JOHN ROMITA, SR., STEVE DITKO, GENE COLAN, MARIE SEVERIN & RON FRENZ** INCREDIBLE INKS (in order of appearance) by **TOM PALMER, JOE SINNOTT, TERRY AUSTIN, BILL REINHOLD, MARIE SEVERIN & AL MILGROM**

KALEIDOSCOPIC COLORS by **JOHN KALISZ** (with PERFECT PAGE ONE and COLOSSAL COVER COLORING by **PAUL BECTON**) LASCIVIOUS LETTERS by **RICHARD STARKINGS** and **COMICRAFT/AD** EFFERVESCENT EDITS by **MATT IDELSON** ACHING ASSISTANT EDITS by **PAUL TUTRONE** EVIL EDITING-IN-CHIEFING by **BOB HARRAS**

VERY SPECIAL THANKS to: **MARIANO NICIEZA** (who originally conceptualized this project), **DARREN AUCK, SCOTT KOBLISH, GIL KANE** (For additional cover pencils), **THE RAIDERS, AND THE MANY TERRIFIC TALENTS OF THE MIGHTY MARVEL BULLPEN**

HEROES & LEGENDS BASED ON FANTASTIC FOUR ANNUAL #3 BY STAN LEE AND JACK KIRBY

5

THIS TALE, WHICH IS ABOUT TO BEDAZZLE YOUR EYES AND NURTURE YOUR SOUL, IS MORE THAN A MERE SUPER HERO SAGA...

IT IS A PASSIONATE PAEAN TO COMIC BOOK HISTORY!

THROUGH THE MAGIC OF IMAGINATION, WE TAKE YOU BACK THROUGH THE YEARS TO A NEVER-TO-BE-FORGOTTEN EVENT IN THE ANNALS OF MARVEL'S MIGHTIEST HEROES!

HIS NAME IS MARK.

HE'S A RABID SUPERHERO FAN.

BUT HEY, WHO ISN'T?

I CAN'T BELIEVE THEY'RE REALLY GONNA *BE* HERE!

LOOK! THEY'RE STARTING TO ARRIVE!

I'LL BE ABLE T'TELL MY GRAND-CHILDREN I WAS HERE TODAY!

MARK! WAIT FOR ME, SON!

DON'T GET LOST IN THE CROWD!

DON'T WORRY, DAD. I'M OKAY. I JUST DON'T WANNA MISS THE *FANTASTIC FOUR!*

Oh, WOW! LOOK AT THAT!

H-HE'S SO CLOSE -- I CAN ALMOST TOUCH HIM!

THE ANCIENT LEGENDS TOLD OF *HERCULES, SAMSON, DAVID* AND *GOLIATH*...

I SEE THESE SUPER HEROES AND VILLAINS AS THE *NEW* LEGENDS, THE LEGENDS FOR TODAY!

LET THE OTHERS FLEE!

THIS IS *HISTORY* AND I'M PART OF IT!

ALTHOUGH IT'S *THE DAILY GLOBE* THAT PAYS ME...

...IT'S *FUTURE GENERATIONS* THAT WILL BE IN MY DEBT!

FOR THE WORLD MUST NEVER FORGET THIS EPIC BATTLE BETWEEN GOOD AND EVIL!

WHILE PHIL SHELDON PHILOSOPHIZES...

...*CAPTAIN AMERICA* FIGHTS FOR HIS LIFE AGAINST THE STRANGULATING EMBRACE OF *PLANT MAN!*

HE MUST NOT DEFEAT ME!

THE FATE OF A CITY IS AT STAKE!

GREAT SHOOTING, HAWKEYE!

TELL ME SOMETHIN' I DON'T KNOW!

NOW STAY OUTTA THE *WAY*, HEAR?

AS PHIL RUSHES AWAY...

YOUR PUNY POWER CANNOT MATCH THAT OF *THE ENCHANTRESS!*

MAYBE NOT, BUT *QUICKSILVER'S* ON THE WAY!

THE *SCARLET WITCH!* I WONDER IF I CAN --

NO *WAY!* I'M *OUT* OF HERE!

AFTER THIS, I USE A *TELEPHOTO* LENS!

BET YOU THOUGHT WE FORGOT ABOUT LITTLE MARK!

HEY, WE DIDN'T GET WHERE WE ARE TODAY BY BEING FORGETFUL!

CAN'T FIND MY DAD!

EVERYONE'S GONE!

WHY IS IT SO *QUIET* HERE?

MARK GETS HIS ANSWER SOONER THAN HE EXPECTED!

OH NO! NOT *YOU!*

NOT YOU!

14

CONTINUED ON PAGE 17!!

Introducing the wall-crawling, web-slinging, web-headed, wise-cracking, erm...wonderful --

SPIDER-MAN

HOW HE GAINED HIS POWERS...

While on a science trip, high school nerd, *Peter Parker*, was bitten by an irradiated spider, which granted him amazing *arachnid-like* powers!

WITH GREAT POWER...

After a thief murdered his beloved *Uncle Ben*, Peter vowed always to use his awesome abilities to aid his fellow man! Like his uncle once said, *"With great power must come great responsibility."*

BAD PRESS...

Despite dedicating his life to fighting crime, Spider-Man doesn't get any good headlines in the Daily Bugle, where the hard-nosed editor-in-chief, *J. Jonah Jameson*, believes the web-slinger to be a menace...

PICTURE THIS...

However, Spidey's alias Peter Parker works at the Bugle as a photographer... mainly taking pictures of ol' web-head himself! Crazy, or what?

HEY, I CAN SEE MY HOUSE FROM UP HERE!

WITH GREAT **POWER** COMES GREAT **RESPONSIBILITY**

FIVE AMAZING SPIDER-MAN FACTS:

1. He can lift over 10 tonnes! 2. Spidey has reflexes 40 times quicker than a normal human! 3. He can cling to sheer vertical surfaces with his hands and feet! 4. Has a spider-sense, which warns him of any looming danger! 5. Wrist-mounted web-shooters -- ideal for snaring bad guys, or for web-swinging across town!

WEB ADDRESS!

Write the names of Spidey's *friends* and *foes* below into the empty spaces and then the yellow boxes will reveal his *most feared enemy!*

1. THING
2. DOCTOR OCTOPUS
9. LIZARD
8. HOBGOBLIN
3. MARY JANE
4. ELECTRO
11. KRAVEN
5. AUNT MAY
7. J JONAH JAMESON
6. KINGPIN
10. DAREDEVIL

ANSWERS ON PAGE 62 >>>

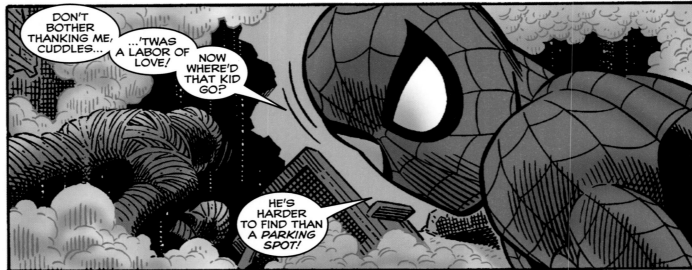

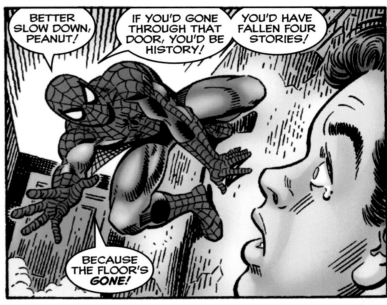

THAT'S WHY A TYRANT LIKE YOU WILL *NEVER* DEFEAT US! BECAUSE WE'RE A *TEAM!*

SPOKEN LIKE THE WITLESS FEMALE YOU ARE!

YOU ARE A TEAM OF NOTHING BUT *FOOLS* AND *BUNGLERS!*

MY *HOLOGRAM* WILL PROVE MY WORDS! BEHOLD!

GOTTA MAKE SURE EVERYTHING'S OKAY IN THERE!

I'VE BEEN *WAITING* FOR YOUR ARRIVAL!

SURRENDER TO THE FORCES OF *HYDRA* OR THE MINISTER *DIES!*

AIN'T NOTHIN' I CAN DO! I-I GOTTA GIVE UP!

A SPLIT SECOND LATER...

I MAY NOT BE ABLE TO *SEE* --

BUT I *HEARD* WHAT YOU SAID -- YOU COWARDLY BRUTE!

ALICIA!

YA SAVED ME, BABY! YA SAVED YOUR BLUE-EYED, BLUSHIN' LOVER BOY!

IF I KNEW YOU'D CRUSH MY RIBS, I MIGHT HAVE THOUGHT TWICE, YOU BIG LUG!

SEE, MR. DOOM, EVEN A BLIND SCULPTRESS CAN HELP DEFEAT YOUR PLANS!

IF I WERE THERE IN PERSON, YOU WOULDN'T DARE SPEAK SO! THE NAME IS DOCTOR DOOM!

SEE THE FEAR MY HOLO-GRAPHIC FORM CAN STILL INSPIRE!

BEWARE THE DAY I APPEAR IN THE FLESH!

WHAT FLESH, YOU MURDEROUS MANIAC?! YOUR BODY -- AND HEART -- ARE AS COLD AND LIFELESS AS THAT METAL ARMOR YOUR WEAR!

DON'T GOAD ME, WOMAN! BEWARE MY WRATH!

THIS IS WHAT I THINK OF YOUR WRATH! AND OF YOUR HOLOGRAPHIC PARLOR TRICKS! SOME DAY THE FF WILL OBLITERATE YOU AS EASILY AS THIS STUPID LITTLE SPY DRONE!

AND NOW, MIRIAM, IT SEEMS MY WEDDING WILL HAVE TO WAIT!

PLEASE HAND ME MY FF UNIFORM!

CONTINUED ON PAGE 35!!

29

DOCTOR DOOM'S BRAIN SCIENCE!

Yes, it is I, Doctor Doom -- future ruler of your world! To find out if you are worthy to be my slave, I have set you these impossibly hard brainteasers to complete!

Are you up to the task? Or are you going to start crying for your mummy?! Ha-ha-haa!

DATA FILE: DOCTOR DOOM!

Real Name: Victor Von Doom

Doctor Doom is a scientific genius and criminal mastermind! He rules his homeland Latveria with an iron fist, and plans to extend his tyranny throughout the world!

FILE 1: OBSERVATION!

Look at the two photos of the world's stupidest superheroes -- the Avengers! Can you spot the SEVEN changes I've made to one of the pictures?

HE WHO DARES, WINS!

Surf the universe!

FANG-TASTIC SPIDERS!

ANGER MANAGEMENT!

THUNDER AND LIGHTNING!

FILE 2: PROBLEM SOLVING!

Below are some books written by famous superheroes! Can you work out which hero wrote which book just by reading the titles?

FILE 3: PATHFINDER!

Can you find your way through the maze below, avoiding all my DOOM BOTS?

START

FINISH

MARVEL COLOUR UP!

Use this colour guide to help with your colouring!

Introducing the Man Without Fear -- DAREDEVIL!

REAL NAME:
Matthew Michael Murdock
OCCUPATION:
A Lawyer by day,
an adventurer at night
BASE OF OPERATIONS:
Hell's Kitchen,
New York City

Matt Murdock lost his eyesight at a young age when he saved an old man from being hit by a truck.

As the truck passed, some toxic waste from its payload splashed into Matt's eyes. However, despite being blinded, Matt soon discovered he had gained superhuman senses!

BILLY CLUB!
His only weapon, Daredevil's cane can be used as a powerful club or grappling hook!

HEROIC HEARING!
Daredevil's hearing is so accurate he can recognise people by listening to their heartbeat!

SUPER TOUCH!
Daredevil's touch is so finely tuned he can read a book just by touching the ink on the paper!

RADAR!
Although blind, Daredevil can sense outlines of objects within a 30-meter radius!

SENSING TROUBLE!
Use your super senses to find Daredevil's enemies listed below, hidden in the word search!

BULLSEYE   KINGPIN   THE OWL

GLADIATOR   MR FEAR   TYPHOID

```
B U L L S E Y E K
L D I O H P Y T I
Y W M R F B I A N
G W O Q E P K U G
G X Z E N H E D P
H S G Y I E T W I
G B T N H T D F N
R O T A I D A L G
```

HE'S OVER *THERE*, SCOTT!

I *HEAR* YOU, LADY!

HELP! THEY'VE GONE *BERSERK!*

PLEASE! SOMEONE *SAVE* US FROM THE *X-MEN!*

BUT IT'S NOT THE PUBLIC THAT'S IN DANGER --

-- AS CYCLOPS' *OCULAR BLAST* FINDS ITS MARK!

THIS IS ONE BATTLE THAT THE EVIL *BATROC* WILL NEVER FINISH!

YOU *SAVED* THEM FROM BATROC --

-- BUT THEY *STILL* FEAR AND DESPISE US!

FACE IT, JEAN -- THE *X-MEN* WILL NEVER WIN A POPULARITY CONTEST!

BUT IT'S SO *UNFAIR!*

WHY DO PEOPLE *HATE* THOSE WHO ARE -- DIFFERENT?

NOT *EVERYONE* DOES -- ONLY THOSE WHOSE MINDS ARE CLOUDED BY FEAR AND IGNORANCE!

44

LONGTIME READERS OF MARVEL'S MONSTER MAGS WILL HAVE NO TROUBLE RECOGNIZING --

-- THE MIGHTIEST MONSTER OF ALL --

GROGOOM!

RIGID WITH SHOCK AND TERROR... ...THE BOY IS FROZEN TO THE SPOT ...

...KNOWING HE IS DOOMED!

THAT KID'LL BE CRUSHED!

OR WORSE!

CAN'T REACH HIM IN TIME!

HE'S UNLEASHING A BLAST OF DEADLY FLAME --

RIGHT AT THE BOY!

SHOOM

46

CONTINUED ON PAGE 50!!

HALL OF FAME

Introducing a group of mutant heroes dedicated to protecting a world that both fears and despises them --

THE X-MEN

PROFESSOR X

One of Earth's most powerful *mutant minds*, Charles Xaiver possesses *telepathic* abilities beyond our understanding. He believes man and mutant should co-exist *peacefully* together, and educates young mutants at his *School For Gifted Youngsters* to use their powers to aid mankind.

JEAN GREY

Like Scott, *Jean Grey* was one of the first to join Xavier's school and is a *guiding force* within the X-Men. As well as a *brilliant telepath*, she also has the ability to *levitate* herself and others!

BEAST

He may look as though he should be kept in a cage, but looks can be misleading! *Dr Henry McCoy* is a *scientific genius* and *world-renowned biochemist* whose mutant abilities include *superhuman strength*, speed and agility!

CYCLOPS

Scott Summers is long time *team leader* of the X-Men, and was one of Xaiver's first students. Scott shoots *optical blasts* whenever he opens his eyes, and has to wear *ruby-quartz visors* to help control his mutant ability!

WOLVERINE

Wolverine possesses *animal-like senses* and a *superhuman healing factor!* His entire skeleton, including his *retractable claws*, has been bonded with a virtually indestructible metal called *Adamantium!* All this, plus a *ferocious temper* make him one of the world's most *dangerous mutants!*

STORM

Ororo Munroe is a mutant with the ability to *control the weather* around her! She can create tornadoes and blizzards, temperature changes and produce *electrical storms!*

WHILE THE X-MEN TAKE A BREATHER...

...THE FUN 'N' GAMES CONTINUES AROUND TOWN!

YOU'RE HIDE IS *MINE*, RICHARDS!

YOU CAN'T FIGHT *BOTH* OF US AT ONCE!

HE WON'T *HAVE* TO, BEETLE!

-- LONG AS I'VE GOT MY *FORCE FIELD!*

GOOD WORK, HONEY! NOW I CAN PUT *BLACK KNIGHT* OUT OF ACTION!

AND *I'LL* MAKE SURE THE BEETLE STAYS DOWN FOR THE COUNT!

BUT HOW MANY *MORE* DO WE HAVE TO FIGHT?!

AS THE BATTLE CONTINUES, AN ALIEN PAIR OF EYES OBSERVES EVERY DETAIL...

THOUGH THEY FIGHT WITH VALOR, EARTH'S MIGHTY SUPER HEROES ARE GRAVELY OUT-NUMBERED!

52

54

GO YOU THEN REED RICHARDS! YOU HAVE CHOSEN WISELY... ...AS I KNEW YOU WOULD!

IF THIS WORKS -- -- ALL MEMORY OF THE BATTLE WILL BE ERASED FROM THE PUBLIC'S MIND!

RATHER THAN FORCE OF ARMS -- HOW MUCH BETTER TO DEFEAT THEM BY -- SCIENCE!

WE ARE MORE NUMEROUS. MORE MERCILESS! VICTORY IS WITHIN OUR GRASP!

NEVER! NOT WHILE I HAVE THE MEANS TO DISPLACE YOU ALL -- TO ANOTHER TIME!

NEXT DAY...*

Daily Globe

FANTASTIC WEDDING OF REED AND SUE RICHARDS

YEAH, I KNOW IT'S MUSHY! BUT HEY, SO WHAT?

*WELL, IT'S BETTER THAN "MEANWHILE!"

ANYWAY, I SAW CAPTAIN AMERICA AND LOTSA HEROES!

MAN, SOME GUYS HAVE ALL THE LUCK!

SPORTS
CRAFTSMEN BEAT BULLPEN 10-0

IZZIT TRUE YOU SAW THE X-MEN, TOO?

ARE THEY AS BAD AS EVERYONE SAYS? WERE YOU SCARED OF 'EM?

I'LL NEVER BELIEVE ANY DUMB RUMORS AGAIN! THOSE GUYS ARE THE GREATEST!

THEY SAVED ME -- AND A LOTTA OTHER PEOPLE, TOO!

SPORTS
CRAFTSMEN BEA
BULLPEN 10-0

YOU MEAN -- YOU'RE A FAN NOW?

WHADDA YOU THINK?!

58

Introducing the world's First Family of super heroes...

FANTASTIC FOUR

Whilst on an experimental spaceship, Reed Richards, Sue Richards, Jonny Storm and Ben Grimm were all exposed to high levels of cosmic radiation! After crash landing to earth, all four suddenly discovered they possessed fantastic new powers...!

Invisible Woman!

Sue Richards has the ability to control cosmic energy, turning herself and others around her completely invisible!

She can also create protective force fields and fly by projecting columns of psonic force!

Mister Fantastic!

A superhuman genius in almost all scientific fields, Reed Richards can alter his body into a highly supple state, allowing him to stretch, deform, and reform himself into virtually any shape!

The Human Torch!

Younger brother of Sue, Jonny Storm has the ability to cover his body in fiery plasma, fly at supersonic speeds, and can even fire nova flame bursts! He can also control heat and flames not of his own making!

The Thing!

When Ben Grimm was exposed to the cosmic radiation his skin turned into an orange, flexible, rock-hard material! He also discovered he gained superhuman strength, stamina and durability!

WHICH HERO ARE YOU?

Have you ever wondered which Marvel character you are most like? I bet you have!
Well now you can find out just by answering the questions on this page!

1 It's your first day back at school after the summer holidays, which subject are you most looking forward to?

a) Definitely physics! And chemistry! Oh, and maths...all of them!

b) I don't like any of the subjects, but I do like lunchtime!

c) Football, rugby, tennis, cross-country, swimming, athletics -- all of the sports!

d) None! School is so boring, there's nothing I can learn that I don't already know!

2 When your teacher asks you what was the best thing you did during the summer break, what do you say?

a) You invented a machine that can calculate how many stars there are in the universe!

b) You helped you dad build a brick wall!

c) You went to a summer camp where you played lots of sports and made loads of friends!

d) You devised the perfect plan to make all of mankind obey your every word!

3 It is lunchtime and one of the school bullies demands your lunch! What do you do?

a) Tell a teacher. After a stiff telling off, he will never bother you again!

b) Laugh at the bully and demand his lunch instead!

c) Quickly scoff your food down so there's nothing left for him to eat!

d) See if the bully wants to come and work for you as one of your henchmen!

4 When you arrive home from school your mum asks you to do your homework and tidy your room! How so you respond?

a) Kindly inform your mother that you completed your homework on the bus home and that your room is always spotless!

b) Cram everything into your cupboard so the room looks tidy and then make your little sister do your homework!

c) Beg her to let you go out and play with your friends instead! If that fails, beg some more...!

d) Laugh in her face! How dare she ask you to do such tedious tasks!

5 The day is over and it's time for bed! What is the best thing about going to sleep?

a) You're only hours away from getting up, going to school and learning lots!

b) You get to dream about beating up bullies all night!

c) It gives your body a chance to rest so that you're fit for the next day!

d) You can dream about world domination without anyone interfering!

Now turn the page to find your Marvel counterpart...

ANSWERS!

Hey, bub! Don't even think about looking at this page until you've finished the puzzles!

16
WEB ADDRESS!
Spider-Man's most feared enemy is the GREEN GOBLIN!

30-31
DOCTOR DOOM'S BRAIN SCIENCE!

FILE 1: OBSERVATION!
The seven changes made to the Avengers picture are circled here:

FILE 2: PROBLEM SOLVING!

SURF THE UNIVERSE!
Was by the Silver Surfer

ANGER MANAGEMENT!
Was by the Hulk

HE WHO DARES, WINS!
Was by Daredevil

THUNDER AND LIGHTNING!
Was by Thor

FANG-TASTIC SPIDERS!
Was by the Spider-Man

61
WHICH HERO ARE YOU?
How did you answer?

MOSTLY A'S = INTELLECTS!
Just like Reed Richards and Professor X, you are one of the universe's great minds!

MOSTLY B'S = POWERHOUSES!
You're not the brightest spark around, but you've more than made up for it in bulk!

MOSTLY C'S = DAREDEVILS!
Forget homework, you would prefer to be playing sports with your friends any day!

MOSTLY D'S = PURE EVIL!
Hero? Forget that! You sound more like a super villain to me!

34 SENSING TROUBLE!

```
B U L L S E Y E E   K
L D I O H P Y Y T   I
Y W M R F E A R R   N
G W O Q B I U P     G
G X Z E P K W Z     P
H S G Y H E D T     I
G B G N E T F W     N
R O T A I D A L     G
```

HERO LOGOS! DID YOU FIND THEM ALL?
There are 5 Fantastic Four logos!

4